Dedicated to my cousin David

Thank you for being you!

My name is Squiggles!

AND MY NAME IS LINE

I like to squiggle around in my own way,

I DON'T LIKE TO CROSS THE LINE

Whenever I make
a mistake,
I think of it as
a way to learn

I DON'T LIKE
MISTAKES AT ALL,
THEY DO ME
NO GOOD

IF SOMEONE IS
MEAN TO ME I
DO THE SAME
FOR THEM

If someone lets
me down I
am nice back

IF SOMEONE HATES ME, I HATE THEM TOO

If someone shows me hate, I show them love

11

I like to shine bright,
I am beautiful just
the way I am

IF I AM NOT BEAUTIFUL,
I AM NOT BEAUTIFUL.
I CAN NOT AND WILL
NOT CHANGE

When I lose,
I say
"good game"

I DO **NOT** LIKE
LOSING, THE OTHER TEAM
SHOULDN'T WIN

IF SOMEONE WHO
WAS NOT NICE TO
ME IS HURT, I
LEAVE THEM HANGING

If someone who
is mean to me is
in trouble, I help,
it is a much better
way to make friends

17

Sometimes people are
Squiggles and other times,
they are Lines,
Just remember:
You have a choice

Who do YOU want to be?

Made in the USA
Middletown, DE
07 May 2021